CW00429409

The Alternative Baby Keepsake Book

Laugh Out Loud Memories from Baby's First Year

Esther Onions

Illustrations by Peter King

Copyright © 2018 Esther Onions

The moral right of the author has been asserted.

Apart from any fair dealing for the purposes of research or private study, or criticism or review, as permitted under the Copyright, Designs and Patents Act 1988, this publication may only be reproduced, stored or transmitted, in any form or by any means, with the prior permission in writing of the publishers, or in the case of reprographic reproduction in accordance with the terms of licences issued by the Copyright Licensing Agency. Enquiries concerning reproduction outside those terms should be sent to the publishers.

ISBN 978 1999758 905

British Library Cataloguing in Publication Data.
A catalogue record for this book is available from the British Library.

Published by Stone House Publishing
www.alternativebabybook.co.uk

'How could something so small create so
much of something so disgusting?'

Steve Guttenberg, 'Three Men and a Baby'

The Alternative Baby Keepsake Book

Laugh Out Loud Memories from Baby's First Year

Having a baby is a beautiful, life-changing event, but it also brings with it a whole nappyful of funny, embarrassing and very, *very* smelly moments. From the most cack-handed comment Dad made in the delivery room to Baby's first poo-tastrophe in public, with The Alternative Baby Keepsake Book you can record the incidents that will become part of family folklore long after Baby's first solid food has been forgotten.

Not only will you have huge fun filling in this book, you can look forward to sharing it with your beloved sproglet many years from now. Just call it payback time for all the mortifying moments they caused you!

From Beer To Maternity

Mum's full name (including any unfortunate middle names):

....

Mum's date of birth: ....

Oh, pur-lease!
Now the real date: ....

How many serious boyfriends did mum have before Dad? ☐

And the rest! Tip: **multiply** the answer above by three: ☐

Dad's full name (including any unfortunate middle names):

....

Dad's date of birth: ....

How many serious girlfriends did Dad have before Mum? ☐

In his dreams! Tip: **divide** the answer above by three: ☐

How did they meet? ....

....

Mum's first impressions of Dad:

A) Phwoar! ☐

B) Well hellooo! ☐

C) Uhm... ☐

D) Eek! ☐

E) Other: ....

Her first words to him were:

....

Dad's first impressions of Mum:

A) Phwoar! ☐

B) Phwoar! ☐

C) Phwoar! ☐

D) Phwoar! ☐

E) Other: ....

His first words to her were:

....

So, um, do you come here often?

Only every day for the past five years...

Their first date was on: ....

They went to: ....

How'd it go?

A) It was sensational from start to finish ☐

B) **It was awkward as a cow on roller-skates at first, but got better** ☐

C) **It was a bit meh** ☐

D) It was a disaster (so much so it remains a mystery why they ever went on a second date) ☐

E) Other: ....

Mum, what's the first thing that comes into your head when you think of Dad?

....

....

Dad, what's the first thing that comes into your head when you think of Mum?

....

....

Photo

Photo

Mum and Dad in the innocent days before
sleep deprivation and noxious nappies

Up The Duff Stuff

When was Baby conceived?

A) After a few years ☐

B) After a few months ☐

C) After a few days ☐

D) After a few hours ☐

E) Other: ....

How did Dad find out Mum was pregnant?

A) She showed him a positive pregnancy test ☐

B) She did something quirky like spelling it out in alphabetti spaghetti ☐

C) She whispered it to him just before they said their marriage vows ☐

D) He spotted a post she'd made about it on social media ☐

E) Other: ....

....

When Dad found out, did he:

A) Cheer ☐

B) Weep ☐

C) Faint ☐

D) All of the above ☐

E) Other: ....

Did Mum experience any pregnancy side-effects?

A) More mood swings than a toddler's birthday party ☐

B) More wind than a baked bean convention ☐

C) More stretch marks than a rubber band factory ☐

D) Feeling sicker than a parrot with bird flu ☐

E) Enough zits to fill a secondary school cafeteria ☐

F) Other: ....

....

Did Mum have any cravings?

A) Strong smells – she could have snorkelled in white spirit ☐

B) Fast food – the faster she could shove it in her mouth, the better ☐

C) Crazy combinations like banana and ketchup sandwiches ☐

D) She really dug earth ☐

E) Chocolate. More chocolate. A bit more chocolate. Oh, and some chocolate to finish ☐

F) Just food. Any kind, as long as there was enough to fill a large bucket ☐

G) Other: ....

I was told there
would be glow...

What did Mum miss when pregnant?

A) Her feet ☐

B) Cigarettes/booze ☐

C) A normal bladder (as opposed to one roughly the size of a kitten's) ☐

D) Wild, swinging-from-the-chandeliers sex ☐

E) Her regular knickers (rather than ones you could use to hand glide off a mountain) ☐

F) Being able to shave her legs and mini-moo ☐

G) Other: ....

Most ridiculous old wives' tale Mum heard:

A) Bad indigestion? Your baby will have more hair than a longboat of Vikings ☐

B) If you have big feet you'll have an easy labour ☐

C) Don't wear high heels – your baby will go cross-eyed ☐

D) Don't raise your arms over your head – the umbilical cord could get wrapped around your baby's neck ☐

E) Drinking lots of water helps keep your baby clean in the womb... ☐

F) ...but don't drink too much – your baby could drown ☐

G) Other: ....

Who correctly predicted Baby's gender? | And who got it wrong?

.... | ....

.... | ....

Most cack-handed comment Dad made during the pregnancy:

A) It's due when? But that's the day of the Cup Final! ☐

B) Ahoy mateys, thar she blows! ☐

C) Ooh, my back's killing me too. Give it a rub, will you? ☐

D) Sorry, I ate the last piece ☐

E) You want to discuss baby names *again*? ☐

F) Woo-hoo, your boobs are finally big! ☐

G) Other: ....

Best baby shower present:

A) Condoms ☐

B) Nappies ☐

C) Air freshener ☐

D) Haemorrhoid cream ☐

E) Enough chocolate to make a dentist quiver in anticipation ☐

F) This book ☐

G) Other: ....

KICKASS COMEBACKS TO PERSONAL PREGNANCY COMMENTS

Was it planned?
Were you?

Blimey, you're massive!
Thanks - can I borrow your clothes?

You must be having a girl as girls steal your beauty
I take it **you've got girls, then?**

Can I feel your belly?
Sure, as long as I can feel yours

What are you hoping for?
A dinosaur, of course

...AND IF YOU'RE EXPECTING TWINS OR MORE

You're going to have your hands full
You're right! I'll think about sending one back

Well, at least you're done now
I didn't know there was a law about how many children I can have

How'd you manage that, then?
Oh, we just went at it like a couple of sex-starved rabbits

Are they natural?
No, they're cyborgs

Most inappropriate thing someone said to Mum:

....

Her response at the time:

....

And, after stewing it over for hours, the badass response she wished she'd come out with:

....

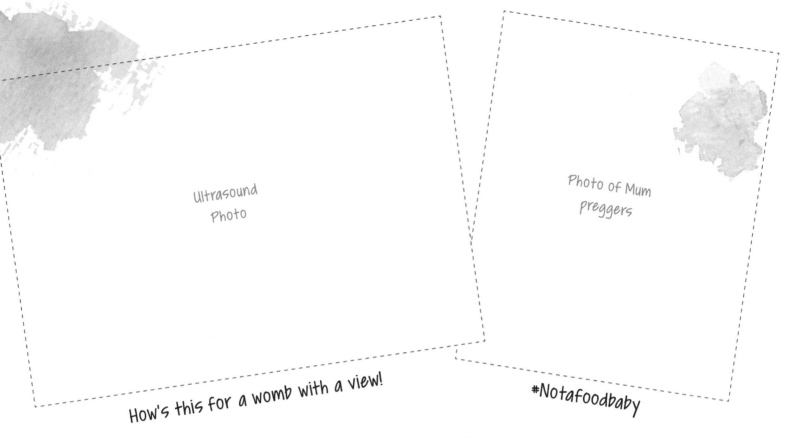

Ultrasound Photo

How's this for a womb with a view!

Photo of Mum preggers

#Notafoodbaby

Eviction Notice

Baby was due on:

Baby was born on:

Time of birth:

Place of birth:

....

....

....

....

How big was Baby?

A) Ooh, that smarts ☐

B) OK, this isn't funny anymore ☐

C) OUCH!!! ☐

D) Holy %&$!, I'm giving birth to a watermelon! ☐

E) JUST SHOOT ME NOW! ☐

F) Actual size: ....

Most optimistic item packed in hospital bag:

A) A bumper-sized book of *Sudoku* ☐

B) Aromatherapy oils ☐

C) TENS machine ☐

D) "Relaxing" music ☐

E) A *pre*-pregnancy outfit to go home in ☐

F) A birth plan (LOL) ☐

G) Other: ....

Did Mum try any of these to kick-start labour?

A) Eating something so spicy even Baby started sweating ☐

B) Bouncing on a birthing ball/space hopper/the see-saw at the local playground ☐

C) Frenzied nipple twiddling ☐

D) Stuffing herself with pineapple or glugging raspberry leaf tea ☐

E) Busting some moves to Beyoncé ☐

F) Doing the – *ahem* – business with Dad ☐

G) Other: ....

What was the midwife like?

A) Satan in scrubs ☐

B) Florence Nightingale ☐

C) Other: ....

Mum's thoughts about pain relief **before** the birth:

A) I am a birthing goddess whose body has been perfectly designed to bring a baby into the world without unnecessary medical intervention ☐

B) Other: ....

Mum's thoughts about pain relief **during** the birth:

A) GIVE! ME! DRUGS! ☐

B) Other: ....

Worst moment of the birth for Mum:

A) Various medical staff rummaging around in her vajayjay ☐

B) Attempting to throttle the midwife during a particularly nasty contraction ☐

C) Being told she was too far gone for an epidural ☐

D) Pooping while pushing ☐

E) Dad looking queasy when the midwife ordered him down to the business end ☐

F) Being stitched where the sun don't shine ☐

G) Other: ....

And if it was a C-section:

A) The doctors chatting about their holiday plans while slicing her open ☐

B) Feeling like a small, stubborn octopus was being hauled out of her ☐

C) Dad going green after peeking over the screen ☐

D) The anaesthetic making her shake like cream cake at a slimming club ☐

E) Not being allowed able to eat solids afterwards until she'd had a good fart ☐

F) Being terrified to sneeze/cough/laugh for weeks in case her stitches popped ☐

G) Other: ....

Worst thing Mum said:

A) The next person who touches me will taste knuckles ☐

B) *&% this, I'm going home! ☐

C) If you take away my gas and air, when all this is over I will look for you, I will find you and I will kill you ☐

...And to Dad:

A) Why don't YOU get down here and have this baby! ☐

B) I'm booking you in for the snip tomorrow ☐

C) You %$£*&^! b%stard! ☐

D) Other: ....

That's what got you here in the first place, dear...

Worst thing the midwife said:

A) I was absolutely hammered last night ☐

B) Hang on a min, I've just got to Google this... ☐

C) It's not as much fun coming out as it was going in, eh? ☐

D) Goodness, I don't think I've ever seen a head that big ☐

E) Now, which bit goes where? (while stitching Mum up) ☐

F) Oh dear, I can't seem to find the needle anywhere (after stitching Mum up) ☐

G) Other: ....

12

Worst thing Dad said:

A) Darling, I'm not sure I'm ready for this fatherhood thing... ☐

B) Smile, you're on Facebook! ☐

C) Eww, that's disgusting! ☐

D) Stop overreacting! I'll hold your hand as soon as I've finished my pizza ☐

E) Are you nearly done? Because my feet are killing me ☐

F) So, when do you want to have the next one? ☐

G) Other: ....

Worst thing Dad said **after** the birth:

A) While gazing at Baby: She looks just like my Uncle Colin ☐

B) Now that wasn't so bad, was it? ☐

C) Dear God, it's like a war zone down there ☐

D) So when will you start getting rid of all the baby weight? ☐

E) Right, I'm off down the pub ☐

F) To the midwife: Can you put in an extra stitch for me? ☐

G) Other: ....

Baby looked like:

A) Mum ☐

B) Dad ☐

C) Winston Churchill ☐

D) E.T. ☐

E) The milkman ☐

F) A grumpy potato ☐

G) Other: ....

13

Mum's attitude to visitors:

A) **The more the merrier!** ☐

B) **NO ONE gets in here until I look like I've spent 12 hours in a spa, not 12 hours giving birth!** ☐

C) Other: ....

First photo of Baby

"Why hello! I look forward to getting to know you, especially between the hours of 1 – 4am..."

If Dad wet the baby's head, how messy did it get on a scale of 1-10? (Score 9 immediately if he cried with emotion at any point):

....

Was the placenta used for anything?

A) A delicious pâté (possibly served 'Silence of the Lambs'-style with some fava beans and a nice Chianti) ☐

B) **"Energy boosting" pills for Mum** ☐

C) **A delightful placenta print for the wall** ☐

D) A placenta pendant or other jewellery ☐

E) **It was planted in the garden beneath a new tree** ☐

F) **Eww! It was left at the hospital, thank you very much!** ☐

G) Other: ....

14

I'M RELATED TO WHO?!

Brothers and sisters: Step-brothers and step-sisters:

....

Grandparents:

....

Dismayed family pet(s):

....

Embarrassing family members (who hopefully will never read this book):

....

Newspaper Cutting

Craziest news story on the day Baby was born

NAMING AND SHAMING

Baby's name:

....

Most ridiculous names suggested:

....

She called the poor little sod John. What's wrong with a nice normal name like J'Zayden or Chayse?

Was Baby named after anything?

A) A much-loved relative ☐

B) A consumer item, eg: Ikea, Porsche... Andrex ☐

C) A footballer or team ☐

D) A place, eg: Paris, India... Slough ☐

E) A celebrity baby, eg: North, Apple, Jermajesty ☐

F) Mum and Dad's names combined, eg: Shandy (Sharon and Andy) ☐

G) Other: ....

And after all that hard work, what were Baby's nicknames?

....

Early "Daze"

Baby came home on (date):

....

That first trip can be nerve-racking. How slowly was Baby driven home?

A) Slower than a snail on tranquilisers ☐

B) **Slower than a teenager taking his nan out for an afternoon spin** ☐

C) Slower than a bank robber who's just spotted a police car behind him ☐

D) Other: ....

Baby's umbilical stump fell off on:

....

Envelope

Baby's umbilical stump, because nothing beats a nice biological keepsake

What made Baby happy?

A) Sleep ☐

B) Milk ☐

C) Cuddles ☐

D) Other: ....

....

What made Baby unhappy?
(NB: this list is not exhaustive)

A) Having a nappy change ☐

B) Not having a nappy change ☐

C) Being fussed over ☐

D) Not being fussed over ☐

E) Being hot ☐

F) Being cold ☐

G) Being dressed ☐

H) Being undressed ☐

I) Being tired ☐

J) Being hungry ☐

K) Being windy ☐

L) Seriously, who the hell knows? ☐

M) Other: ....

....

Best baby advice Mum received:

A) You can *never* have too many wet wipes ☐

B) Always carry spare baby clothes. The one day you don't will be the day of a public poo-tastrophe ☐

C) Buttons and bows irritate newborns (as well as making them look like deranged cupcakes) ☐

D) When you remove a nappy, *always* have the next one ready. Otherwise you/the carpet/the cat will suffer the consequences ☐

E) Clothes with loud patterns are much better at hiding baby slobber ☐

F) It gets better. Honestly ☐

G) Other: ....

18

I sleep when he sleeps. I clean when he cleans…

Barmiest baby advice Mum received:

A) Holding a baby too much spoils them ☐

B) Keep your breasts covered to keep your milk warm ☐

C) You can't get pregnant while breastfeeding (oh yes you can!) ☐

D) Putting whiskey on a baby's gums helps with teething pain ☐

E) You need to have another baby ASAP to keep this one company ☐

F) Sleep when your baby sleeps (yes, don't eat, clean or, God forbid, go for a poo) ☐

G) Other: ....

POINTLESS PRODUCTS

Most useless baby product purchased:

A) **Nappy bin** (because everyone just loves the odour of festering nappies in the home) ☐

B) **Baby wipes warmer** (do babies really question the warmth of their wipes when you're scrubbing poo off their backs at 3am?) ☐

C) **Top and tail bowl** (why not go the whole hog and buy an elbow bowl, knee bowl and ankle bowl too?) ☐

D) **A wee cone** (it – and you – will be swiftly peed off) ☐

E) **Nappy stacker** (because nappies don't come stacked in packaging already. Oh, wait...) ☐

F) **Baby shoes** (newsflash: babies can't walk) ☐

G) Other: ....

Best baby product purchased:

....

WEEEEE!!

20

VISITING RIGHTS (AND WRONGS)

Who visited in the first few days?

....

What was the best thing visitors did?

A) Arranged a time to come over rather than just showing up ☐

B) Didn't overstay their welcome ☐

C) Brought food ☐

D) Looked after Baby while Mum took a nap ☐

E) Tackled a few household chores ☐

F) Didn't try to hog Baby the entire visit ☐

G) Other: ....

What was the worst thing visitors did?

A) Turned up with a stinking cold ☐

B) Sat on their backsides expecting to be waited on ☐

C) Stuck their unwashed fingers in Baby's mouth ☐

D) Said they'd only stay ten minutes or so. Left at 2am ☐

E) Insisted on trying to wake Baby ☐

F) Gave constant, unsolicited advice ☐

G) Other: ....

If you wouldn't mind popping one of these on first...

21

Best gift received: ....

Most "What were they thinking?" gift received: ....

Photos of Baby and family

Baby meets the clan

Baby and family

Baby and family

Photos of Baby and friends

Baby meets the gang

Baby and friends

Baby and friends

23

CHIC CHILD OF MINE

Photo:
Baby's first fancy
dress outfit

Photo:
Baby's iffiest outfit

Work it,
Baby!

Photo:
Baby's snazziest outfit
(sunglasses optional)

24

RESISTING A REST

What did Baby's crying sound like?

A) A bleating lamb ☐

B) A snuffling piglet ☐

C) A baby elephant wanting its mum ☐

D) A randy cat ☐

E) A fox getting a strip wax ☐

F) Other: ....

What desperate measures did Mum and Dad use to try and get Baby to sleep?

A) Bribery – "I swear I'll buy you a pony/a Porsche/Disneyland Paris if you just go to sleep now" ☐

B) Fresh air – trudging the streets for hours like pram-pushing zombies ☐

C) Praying – "Dear God, make this baby sleep, and I promise I'll go to church regularly and only drink on days that end in the letter Y" ☐

D) Driving – buckling up Baby for red-eyed road trips ☐

E) Making white noise with a fan, vacuum cleaner or similar – sod the electricity bill, sleep is at stake! ☐

F) And when things got *really* bad, they sang, rocked and hummed in a darkened room. Sometimes they even tried doing this with Baby… ☐

G) Other: ....

25

Commentary by David Attenborough: "And here we have the Lesser Spotted Sleeping Baby, a creature so rare it makes the Loch Ness Monster look like Kim Kardashian"

Photo of Baby asleep

What method did Mum and Dad use to leave the bedroom without waking baby?

A) 'Mission Impossible'-style with a combination of stomach slithering and forward rolls ☐

B) Via a complicated route to avoid creaking floorboards (extra points if they marked these out with cuddly toys) ☐

C) Using the 'quicker is better' approach and hightailing it faster than an Olympic sprinter on steroids ☐

D) They inched out on all fours, freezing mid-shuffle if Baby so much as farted ☐

E) Indiana Jones-style, deftly swapping the arm trapped beneath sleeping Baby for a teddy bear ☐

F) They didn't. It was better to lie down beside the cot than risk the horror of Baby waking up ☐

G) Other: _____

BABY VS FOOD

What was Baby's favourite food in the first year?:

....

And what food did Mum/Dad/the cat invariably end up splattered with?:

....

BABY'S FIRST WORD

What Mum insisted Baby's first word was:

☐
☐

A) Mama

B) Other

What Dad insisted Baby's first word was:

☐
☐

A) Dada

B) Other

What Baby's first word actually was:

....

Photo of Baby "wearing" their meal

What's that? Some food missed my mouth, you say?

MOTHERS' MEETINGS

Best parent and toddler group Mum went to:

....

And the worst:

....

What was wrong with it?

A) It was cliquey ☐

B) It was cliquey ☐

C) It was cliquey ☐

D) Other: ....

E) It was cliquey ☐

Which of the following mum types did Mum encounter?

The competitive one

Whatever skill your baby has developed, competitive mum delights in telling you how little Ellie or George mastered it – "Gosh, when was it now... oh yes, weeks ago." If your baby has just started sitting up, hers is doing backflips; if yours has started bashing a plastic keyboard, hers is a piano prodigy comparable only to the young Mozart. **Irritation factor: 5/5** ☐

The Facebook fanatic

After passing brief inanities in the juice and biscuits queue, this mum will have sent you a friendship request in the time it takes you to sit back down. If you accept – and you feel it'd be rude not to – resign yourself to a stream of trite "inspirational" quotes; attention-seeking vaguebook posts ("Why do ppl always let you down? #Sad ☹..."), and photos of her baby's every single not-so-precious moment. Oh, and pictures of kittens. **Irritation factor: 3/5** ☐

The Earth mother

Little Coriander wears unbleached, organic hemp baby-grows and is only allowed to play with sustainably produced, gender-neutral toys. Or twigs. Despite saying we should all, like, chill, and be more open-minded, this quinoa queen can't resist making disparaging comments about anyone who uses disposable nappies. She's secretly terrified someone will find out she asked for pain relief during childbirth. **Irritation factor: 4/5** ☐

The impossibly glamorous one

While other mums regard rubbing baby snot off their clothes as a huge nod towards sartorial elegance, glamorous mum sashays into the play group all swishy locks and tanned limbs, Prada tote in one manicured hand, pristine tot in the other. Mere mortals console themselves with the thought she must have dragged herself from bed at squirrel's fart to achieve this look. **Irritation factor: 3/5**

The neurotic one

Neurotic mum has yet to learn there's a fine line between devoted and deranged. With an antibacterial wipe clutched in one hand and a bottle of hand sanitiser in the other, she's ready to leap into bacteria-blasting action if her tot so much as touches the floor. Due to being utterly distracted by her baby at all times, when talking to other mums she has never been known to finish a sente... **Irritation factor: 3/5**

The over-sharing one

For some unfathomable reason, this mum thinks you're desperate to know every eye-watering detail of her motherhood experience, from the exact size of her mucus plug to the first time she and her husband had post-baby sex. Try not to gag on your custard cream as she lovingly details the colour and consistency of Theodore's last poop. **Irritation factor: 4/5**

And finally, the awkward dad

There's always at least one bloke doing his best to appear utterly at ease in the oestrogen soup that is a parent and toddler group. He'll be the one massively over-engaging with his sprog, hoping to prove a) He's cool with this and b) He's most definitely not eyeing-up any of the women present. Secretly he believes a few of the mums fancy him thanks to his obvious new mannish charms. **Irritation factor: 2/5**

Best new parent friend Mum made:

....

And the one she'd feign insanity to avoid:

....

ALTERNATIVE MILESTONES

In years to come will anyone – even Baby – really care about the date on which they first drank from a cup or their ninth tooth appeared? These are the milestones you'll never want to forget!

Baby's Alternative Milestones

Yes, I am panning for gold as a matter of fact – the little bugger swallowed my wedding ring!

First foreign object swallowed:

Details: ....

Did it reappear:

A) Whole?

B) In bits?

C) Never reappeared...

First object up nose:

Details: ....

First time rolling off the bed (or similar):

Details: ....

First trip to A&E:

Details: ....

First time biting someone. Hard.

Details: ....

First time pulling a no-sleep all-nighter:

Details: ....

First innocent but obscene hand gesture:

Details: ....

First time grabbing another woman's breasts:

Details: ....

First junk food (after Mum swore it would never pass Baby's lips):

Details: ....

First word that sounded like a swear word:

Details: ....

First overzealous interaction with an innocent domestic animal:

Details: ....

First time saying: "No!"

Details: ....

First public meltdown:

Details: ....

Other alternative firsts:

Details: ....

....

....

....

....

....

....

Mum's Alternative Milestones

First time sitting down without wincing:

Details: ....

First time she didn't feel like an extra from the 'Night of the Living Dead':

Details: ....

First time wearing something other than leisurewear:

Details: ....

First time back in an underwired bra:

Details: ....

First time back in pre-baby jeans:

Details: ....

First time back in pre-baby jeans without doing herself an injury:

Details: ....

First uninterrupted poo (never underestimate the unadulterated joy of this moment):

Details: ....

First time drinking a mug of tea *while it was still hot*:

Details: ....

First time going an entire day without discussing the contents of Baby's nappy:

Details: ....

First time walking around in public blissfully unaware of the two big wet spots on her top:

Details: ....

First time sitting in a draughty church hall singing 'The Wheels on the Bus':

Details: ....

First time she said she'd never give Baby a dummy:

Details: ....

and

First time she gave Baby a dummy:

Details: ....

First outing without Baby:

Details: ....

First time rocking from side to side in public before realising she didn't have Baby with her:

Details: ....

First big night out:

Details: ....

First post-baby raging hangover:

Details: ....

First time she forgot the details of the birth long enough to consider having another baby:

Details: ....

The wipers on the bus go swish, swish, swish...

Dad's Alternative Milestones

First bottle feed:

Details: ....

First time on the 'graveyard shift':

Details: ....

First time holding Baby above their head while singing the 'Circle of Life':

Details: ....

First time dressing Baby in an outfit Mum didn't roll her eyes at:

Details: ....

First uninterrupted sleep of seven hours or more:

Details: ....

First *very* messy night out:

Details: ....
and

First raging hangover after a very messy night out when he remembered he was looking after Baby that day:

Details: ....

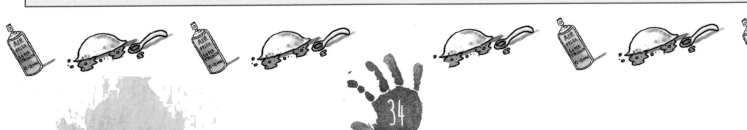

Mum AND Dad's Alternative Milestones

First 'walk of shame' (when Baby is carried back to the living room still wide awake hours after bedtime):

Details:..

First time forgetting to lock the wheels on the buggy:

Details:..

First time accidentally leaving Baby behind:

Details:..

First time they managed an entire day without playing the "I'm more tired than you" card:

Details:..

First night out together:

Details:..

How many times did they contact the babysitter?

A) **They didn't. They knew they'd get a call if there was a problem.** ☐

B) **Once, just to be on the safe side** ☐

C) Between three and ten times, but with big gaps in-between ☐

D) **They decided it was less stressful to cancel the babysitter and stay home instead** ☐

E) Other:..

First post-baby ladies and gentlemen:

....

(Actually, no details necessary. No, REALLY)

Poo, Spew and Goo

First person Baby peed on: ....

First person Baby pooed on: ....

First person Baby puked on: ....

Brrraaapp!

First time Mum/Dad walked around in public oblivious to the steaming splodge of baby gunk down their back:

Details: ....

First earth-shatteringly loud fart in public:

Details: ....

First time Dad tried to blame his earth-shatteringly loud fart in public on Baby:

Details: ....

First poo in the bath:

Details: ....

First time Baby discovered their inner Picasso using their own poo:

Details: ....

First public poo-splosion (when liquid poo erupted from Baby's clothing):

Details: ....

First time Mum/Dad committed the cardinal sin of leaving the house without spare nappies:

Details: ....

and

Most creative thing they used instead (extra points if gaffer tape played a part):

A) Sanitary towels ☐

B) **A regular towel** ☐

C) **Loo roll** ☐

D) **Breast pads** ☐

E) A cuddly toy ☐

F) **An item of clothing** ☐

G) Other: ....

Baby's First Birthday

How was it celebrated?

....

How many times did Mum say "We'll just keep it small" – before inviting everyone she'd ever known?

....

Who got inappropriately drunk?

....

On a scale of 1-10, how bewildered was Baby during the proceedings?

....

Photo: Baby's first birthday

I survived the first 365 days with my parents!

38

_____

_____

_____

_____

_____

Photo

Epic Mum, Dad and Baby Moments, Awesome Quotes and Bloody Brilliant Memories from Baby's First Year

Photo

_____

_____

_____

_____

_____

Photo

Photo

Photo

Photo

41

Photo

Photo

AIR
FRESH
SUPER
STRENGTH
0-12 mths

42